The Duke of Wellington was in the shop!

5

The Duke bought his crisps and went out of the shop.

8

Jamila followed the Duke.
Jamila wanted to see what he did.

The Duke went into a house.

I could look in the window.

Jamila went to the window.
What was going on in the house?

It was a birthday party!
They all sang Happy Birthday.

Jamila went into the Square.